MONSTER HOUSE

Based on the screenplay
by Dan Harmon & Rob Schrab
and Pamela Pettler

Story by Dan Harmon & Rob Schrab

LEVEL 1

Adapted by: Lynda Edwards

Commissioning Editor: Helen Parker

Editor: Diane Winkleby

Cover layout: Emily Spencer

Designer: Victoria Wren

Picture research: Emma Bree

Photo credits: Cover image and inside images provided
courtesy Columbia Pictures Industries, Inc.
Page 32: H. Jones/Alamy.
Page 33: A. Skelley/Corbis; J. L. Magana/AP/Empics.
Page 34: G. Vaughn/Alamy; Winchester Mystery House.
Page 35: Rough Guides/Alamy.
Page 36: D. McCollester/Getty Images.
Page 37: D. McCollester, P. De Voecht/AFP/Getty Images.

Published by Scholastic Ltd. 2007

Printed in Singapore

CONTENTS

PAGE

Monster House	**4–31**
People and places	**4**
Chapter 1: Do you want to die?	**6**
Chapter 2: Come in!	**10**
Chapter 3: We don't believe you!	**14**
Chapter 4: *Domus Mactabilis*	**18**
Chapter 5: Constance the Giantess	**22**
Chapter 6: Mr. Nebbercracker's story	**25**
Chapter 7: Goodbye, Constance!	**28**

Fact Files	**32–37**
Halloween around the world	**32**
Strange houses ... true stories?	**34**
The circus	**36**

Self-Study Activities	**38–40**

MONSTER HOUSE

DJ Walters

DJ Walters lives with his mom and dad in Oak Street, Mayville. He's 12 years old and very clever. He's interested in the strange house across the street.

Chowder

Chowder is DJ's best friend. They do everything together, but many things frighten him. He likes basketball.

Jenny Bennet

Jenny goes to school in Mayville. She's very pretty and she's clever with money. She isn't frightened of any-thing.

Mr. Nebbercracker

Mr. Nebbercracker lives in the house opposite DJ. He's very old and shouts at all the children. He hates people on his lawn.

Bones
Bones is Zee's boyfriend.

Zee
Zee stays with DJ when his mom and dad are away.

Skull
Skull works at Pizza Freek. He's the best computer games player in the world. He knows everything about monsters.

Lister and Landers
Lister and Landers are policemen. They work in Mayville. Lister is a new policeman.

PLACES

Oak Street, Mayville
A street in an American town. DJ and Mr. Nebbercracker live here. It's a pretty place and it's usually very quiet.

Pizza Freek
A cheap restaurant. Skull works here. People also come here to play computer games.

Danger Zone
Builders are building new houses here. DJ and Chowder come here to talk.

MONSTER HOUSE™

Chapter 1
Do you want to die?

It was the afternoon before Halloween*.

A little girl was on her bike in Oak Street in Mayville. She went happily between the trees and the lovely gardens. But then her bike went onto a front lawn and she stopped.

There was a strange sound and she looked up. The lawn was in front of a big old house. There were two windows over the front door. The windows looked down at her angrily.

There was a loud shout and an old man came out of the house. It was Mr. Nebbercracker. 'Get off my lawn!' he shouted, 'Do you want to die?'

* Halloween is on 31st October. Children wear special clothes and ask for treats.

The little girl was frightened and she ran away. Mr. Nebbercracker walked across the lawn and took the bike. 'And don't come back!'

'These children!' he said. 'They never listen.' The sound came again. It was louder and then it stopped. Mr. Nebbercracker went into his house and closed the door.

D J Walters lived opposite Mr. Nebbercracker's house. DJ saw everything and wrote about it in his book. There was a lot of writing in the book. Today he wrote: '30th October. N. took bike.'

'DJ!' his mom called.

'I'm coming!' DJ looked at the pictures on the walls of his bedroom. They were photos of Mr. Nebbercracker's house.

'DJ!' she called again.

DJ ran out of his house. His mom and dad were in the car. 'Mom!' said DJ. 'He took a bike again!'

'DJ,' she said. 'You can't stay in your room for hours to watch an old man.'

'But there's something wrong with that house!'

'We're going,' said his dad. 'Zee is coming soon. She's staying with you tonight.'

'We love you,' called his mom, and they drove away.

Then a boy with a ball came across the street. It was Chowder, DJ's best friend.

'It's Halloween soon,' said Chowder. 'What are you going to wear?'

'I'm not going trick-or-treating this year,' said DJ.

'But we always do.'

'We're too old now.'

Chowder tried to throw his ball into the basket on the wall. He turned and looked at DJ.

'Be careful!' shouted DJ. Chowder turned back and the ball hit him.

'Aghhh!' Chowder put his hand on his nose.

'Are you OK?' asked DJ. Then he saw the ball. 'Oh no!' It was on Mr. Nebbercracker's nice lawn.

'You're older, DJ. You get it,' said Chowder.

'No!' said DJ.

'But it was expensive!'

'Maybe Mr. Nebbercracker is sleeping.' DJ looked at the house. 'OK.' He put one foot on the lawn. The ball was close. He ran to it.

Suddenly the door opened and Mr. Nebbercracker came out. 'You!'

DJ moved quickly. His shoe pulled out a bit of the lawn.

'I'm sorry,' cried DJ. He wanted to run, but Mr. Nebbercracker held his shirt.

'Do you want to die?' shouted Mr. Nebbercracker.

'No. I love life!'

Mr. Nebbercracker pulled DJ's shirt. 'This is my house,' he shouted. 'Stay away!' The old man's face was very red and his eyes went big. Suddenly he fell on top of DJ on the lawn. The old man didn't move.

'Uh-oh,' said Chowder.

Then there was a cold wind, and the door closed loudly.

Chapter 2
Come in!

Some people came and took Mr. Nebbercracker away.
'He's dead because of me!' DJ said to Chowder. 'I feel terrible!'

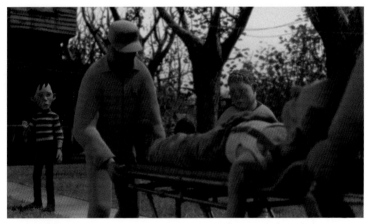

Just then Zee arrived in her car. She took her bag into DJ's house.

'Hi!' she smiled. 'We're going to have a very good time.'

'Mom and dad aren't here,' said DJ.

Zee stopped smiling. 'OK,' she said. 'In the house at nine o'clock. In your room at eleven. No games.'

'I'm not a child!'

Zee just looked at him angrily.

Later, DJ was in his room. He looked at the house across the street. The house looked at him. He saw some smoke – it came out of the top of the house. Then there was a cold wind again and he closed his window.

DJ went to sleep. He had a bad dream about the house. The house came into his room. It was big and dark. Then the dark was a hand. It wanted to …

Suddenly the phone woke him up. DJ looked at the number. He was frightened. The call was from Mr. Nebbercracker's house. Who was it? Then someone was in his room. 'Boo!'

It was Bones, Zee's boyfriend. Bones laughed at DJ. Zee was there, too.

'It isn't funny!' shouted DJ. 'Mr. Nebbercracker's dead and someone is in his house.'

'Oooh!' said Zee and Bones. They didn't believe him. They laughed and left his room.

DJ looked at the house. One of the windows opened, like an eye! DJ's heart went faster. The window closed again. DJ used his phone.

'Police,' answered Chowder.

'The Danger Zone,' said DJ. 'Now!'

Bones told Zee the story of his beautiful red kite. He was ten and he loved that kite more than anything. Bones looked happy, but then his face changed. One day the kite was high in the sky. But then it came down behind the houses. He found it on Mr. Nebbercracker's lawn. The old man shouted at him and took the kite.

'He's a terrible old man,' said Zee.

'Yeah,' said Bones. 'And he's strange. He talked to the house. People say his wife died in that house. Did he eat her?!' He laughed, but Zee was angry. She said, 'Go home, Bones.'

Bones went out of DJ's house. He looked at Mr. Nebbercracker's house. He threw a trainer onto the lawn. Nothing happened. Then he walked on the lawn. He waited. Nothing. He danced on the lawn. 'You are dead!' he shouted. 'Look at me. I'm on your lawn. What are you going to do?'

Suddenly the door opened and Bones saw his lovely red kite. Bones followed it. The door closed and there was a terrible sound. Then it was quiet again.

The Danger Zone was DJ and Chowder's special place. There was a very big crane and a digger and a lot of holes.

'Mr. Nebbercracker is back from the dead,' said DJ. 'He wants to find me! I need your help, Chowder.'

The two boys left the Danger Zone and soon they were in front of Mr. Nebbercracker's house. They saw a trainer on the lawn. The house watched them. Two windows opened slowly. Then nothing.

'This is boring,' said Chowder and he went onto the lawn.

'Don't!' shouted DJ.

Suddenly there was a terrible sound. The door opened and the windows moved. They looked down angrily.

Then the floor opened like teeth in a mouth. There was a big, red open throat. And then the carpet came out of the door like a tongue. The boys ran.

Chapter 3
We don't believe you!

The next morning a young girl came to the door. It was Jenny Bennet.

'You need some treats for tonight,' she said. 'I'm selling chocolates.'

'It's not my house,' said Zee.

'OK,' said Jenny. 'I'm sure the mom and dad left you some money for the trick-or-treaters. You give me $20 for some chocolates. I say you gave me $30. You keep $10 and you can have the chocolates, too.'

'Hey, you're good!' Zee gave Jenny the money.

Zee went to DJ's room. 'What are you doing?' she asked.

'Something in that house tried to eat us,' said DJ. 'We stayed up all night to watch.'

'You're so strange,' said Zee. 'Do you know where Bones is? He left last night and didn't come back.'

'Didn't come back?' said Chowder. 'Zee. I'm sorry, but …'

'The house took your boyfriend,' said DJ.

Zee didn't believe them. She closed her eyes. 'Pleeaase!'

She threw some chocolates to DJ. 'Breakfast,' she said and left the room.

Chowder looked out of the window again. 'Oh,' he said.

DJ looked. It was Jenny. The boys watched her. They liked her red hair. They also liked her little nose and big, clever eyes.

Chowder looked at DJ. 'I saw her first!'

'You can't say that!' said DJ.

'Oh yes, I can!'

Jenny started to go to Mr. Nebbercracker's door with her chocolates.

The boys ran out. 'No!' they shouted.

Jenny looked at them. 'Do you have a problem?' she asked.

Suddenly the windows opened. They were red and angry. Then a terrible cry came from the house and the lawn moved up and down. The door opened and the kids saw the mouth and the teeth. The carpet tongue came out and lifted Jenny up and down. It took the chocolates, but the boys pulled Jenny back.

'Hey!' It was Zee. The lawn and the house went quiet. The door closed. The eyes were windows again.

'I'm going to find Bones.' And she went off.

'What's happening?' asked Jenny.

The boys told Jenny about the house.

'I'm very busy,' said Jenny. 'But that house took my chocolates and tried to eat me … I can give you one hour.'

They all looked at the house. It was quiet now. Then they saw a dog. It walked onto the lawn. The door opened and the tongue came out. It took the dog. It was very quick.

'Call the police,' said Jenny.

Suddenly DJ remembered. 'It's Halloween. Tonight there are going to be a lot of children at that door trick-or-treating! They're all going to die!'

Then the door opened and there was Chowder's ball. Suddenly the ball changed. Now it was a Halloween monster face.

'It's laughing at us,' said Jenny.

Then the police arrived.

There were two policemen. Landers was fat and had a pink face. 'OK. What's happening?' Landers asked.

The other policeman, Lister, was tall. He shouted at them. 'All of you! Next to the car. Now!'

'He's new,' said Landers.

'There's something very bad in that house,' Jenny told them.

'Someone died,' said DJ.

'A dog died, too,' said Chowder.

Landers smiled, but Lister shouted into the police radio, 'Dead dog! Dead dog! We have a problem here!'

Landers took the radio away from him. 'OK, you three. It's Halloween. We're busy.'

DJ tried again. 'Please believe us. The house has a mouth. It pulls things in and eats them!'

'See you later,' said Landers.

'Look!' DJ walked onto the lawn. Nothing. He danced on the lawn. Nothing.

'OK,' said Landers, 'We're going. Leave this house now. I'm going to give you ten. One, two, three …'

'But we need your help,' cried Jenny.

'Four, five, six …'

The three kids looked at the policemen. They weren't going to help. DJ, Chowder and Jenny walked away.

'What can we do now?' asked Chowder.

'I have an idea,' said DJ. 'Let's ask a very clever person.'

Chapter 4
Domus Mactabilis

The Pizza Freek was a cheap restaurant with a lot of computer games. A big man was playing one. His shirt and Pizza Freek hat were dirty.

'This is Skull,' said DJ importantly. 'He knows everything.'

'Let's talk to him,' said Jenny and she walked over to Skull.

He turned. His face was very white and his eyes were red and tired. 'What? I'm busy.'

DJ was quick, 'There's a monster in Mr. Nebbercracker's house. It must die before it eats us.'

'OK, man!' Skull played his game. His hands moved very quickly. 'Sometimes a person loves his house very much. Then he dies. That dead person can live in the house. It's in the walls and the floor. It's called *Domus Mactabilis*.'

'That means Monster House,' said Jenny.

'I knew that,' said Chowder.

'Can we stop it?'asked DJ.

'Find the heart of the house. The heart must die.'

'So, where's the heart?' asked Chowder. No one answered.

Then DJ remembered. 'Smoke comes from the house. The heart of the house must be the fire. We must stop the fire!'

'We don't have much time,' said Jenny. 'We must find a way to get in.'

'I've got an idea!' said DJ. 'First let's make something. It must be like a person. We put Sleep Easy drink in it. The house eats the "person" and goes to sleep. Then we go in and find the fire!'

'That's a very stupid plan,' said Chowder. 'I don't want to go into a monster.'

Jenny looked at DJ. 'It's good. Let's do it.'

'OK,' said Chowder quickly. 'Let's do it.'

DJ found an old carpet cleaner, and Jenny put some clothes on it. It was like a Halloween monster. They put some Sleep Easy drink into the cleaner. They were ready.

It was evening. The tops of the houses were red in the sun.

'Trick or treat?' Chowder called to the house.

The windows opened and looked at the carpet cleaner. There was hate in the eyes.

'Start the cleaner,' said DJ quietly.

The carpet cleaner started to move. It went to the front door. The door opened, and there were the teeth. Ready. Waiting. DJ, Chowder and Jenny smiled.

Suddenly they heard the sound of a police car. The house's eyes and mouth closed, and the carpet cleaner stopped in front of the door.

Landers saw the carpet cleaner. 'What's this?' He looked at it and found the Sleep Easy drink. 'OK. You're going to the police station.'

Lister shouted, 'Right! In the car!'

'Listen to us!' shouted DJ. 'The house is a monster!'

The policemen put the three kids into the car. 'And don't try to open the doors, because you can't,' said Lister.

Suddenly a terrible sound came from the house. 'What's that?' Lister walked to the door. Landers followed him.

'No! Get away from the house!' shouted DJ. He and Jenny tried to open the car doors.

'He's right,' said Jenny. 'We can't get out!'

Chapter 5
Constance the Giantess

Lister ran onto the lawn. It moved. A tree near him started to move, too. He tried to run, but the tree pulled him back. Suddenly he was high in the sky. 'Help!' he called.

Landers tried to run to the car. But the carpet tongue came through the door and pulled him in. Then the tree threw Lister into the house after him.

The kids didn't want to look. The tree took the car and held it high over the lawn. The front door mouth was bigger now.

'I'm only here because of you, DJ!' shouted Chowder.

'No, you're not. You're here because of her!' cried DJ. The car was closer to the mouth.

'Be quiet!' said Jenny. 'We've got a big problem!'

The tree threw the car into the house. The teeth closed on the front of the car. The three kids looked down the red throat. There were teeth all the way down.

'Quick! Move!' shouted DJ. The back window of the car was open. They went through it. Then the door of the house closed and the car went down the throat.

Everything went quiet. The carpet sat quietly on the stairs. The walls and the floors were in the right places.

'It doesn't know we're here,' said DJ quietly. 'Now we must find the fire and put water on it.'

'I don't think that's a good idea,' said Chowder.

'Do you want to die?' asked DJ.

'OK. OK. Let's look for the heart,' Chowder said.

'Be careful,' said DJ. 'And stay togeth…' Suddenly DJ fell through the floor. There was a loud, breaking sound, and Jenny and Chowder fell through after him into the dark.

They were in a big room. There were a lot of children's things there.

'Look at this,' said DJ. It was an old circus caravan. The colours were now old and dark. It was in two parts. On one part of the caravan were some words: 'Constance the Giantess*.' The kids looked at it quietly.

'This was beautiful a long time ago,' said DJ. 'Let's look in it.'

'Let's not,' said Chowder.

DJ went in. There were pictures on the walls.

Then he saw something in the cement floor. It looked like a big body.

Suddenly the floor moved. 'The floor's breaking!'

* A giantess is a very big, tall woman.

shouted DJ. Then there was a strong wind.

'It's Constance,' cried Jenny. 'She's angry. She doesn't like people near her.'

Everything in the room started to move and break. The sounds were terrible. Constance knew they were there.

The wind threw the three kids out of the room.

'Run!' shouted DJ.

Chowder was at the top of the stairs. The throat opened. Suddenly the stairs went down the throat. The throat pulled at Chowder, too. The house gave a terrible cry, but Chowder didn't fall. He held one of the teeth. DJ tried to pull him up. Then the carpet tongue came out quickly and threw DJ down the throat.

'No!' cried Jenny. The house moved up and down. Then she saw something red at the back of the throat. She pulled on it hard. The house moved up and down again.

'I can't hold ...,' she shouted and fell down the red throat. But there was someone close. It was DJ. Jenny held onto his legs. DJ held onto Chowder's legs. Then a strong wind and a lot of water came up the throat. It threw the three kids out of the open door. DJ ran into the street as a car stopped in front of the house.

Chapter 6
Mr. Nebbercracker's story

It was Mr. Nebbercracker. He was very white.

'No!' cried Chowder. 'You're dead. Go away!'

'You go away,' said Mr. Nebbercracker angrily.

'He's not dead,' said DJ happily.

'Of course I'm not dead. Is it Halloween today? Go away or you're going to die!' Mr. Nebbercracker turned to the house. 'I'm home, my love.' The house started to cry.

'Look at your windows and your walls,' he said quietly. 'But it isn't a problem. We can make it better. We're going to have a nice, quiet evening. Like every year. No children – only us.'

'It's her,' said DJ. 'The house is her. Mr. Nebbercracker, I know about Constance. I saw her.'

There was a surprised sound from the house.

'Were you in my house?' cried Mr. Nebbercracker.

'I know she died,' said DJ.

'I loved her,' said Mr. Nebbercracker sadly. He told them Constance's story. The kids saw the pictures in their heads …

They were in Constance's caravan at the circus. There was happy music and circus sounds. People looked at Constance the Giantess in her caravan. They laughed and threw things at her. She was sad and alone. She looked at the floor and tried to forget the people.

One day a boy threw old vegetables at her. Constance was very angry and she shouted at the boy. A young man came and held the boy's arm. It was Mr. Nebbercracker. That night he went to Constance's caravan and they talked. He thought she was beautiful. Mr. Nebbercracker took Constance's caravan away from the circus. They found a place to build a home.

Mr. Nebbercracker started to build a lovely house and made a big hole for the cement. The cement was almost ready. He decided to break Constance's caravan. Then something terrible happened. He heard a loud cry. It was Halloween and some young children came to trick-or-treat. When they saw Constance, they started to throw things at her.

'Go away!' shouted Mr. Nebbercracker.

Some of the things hit Constance. The children just laughed.

'It's always going to be like this,' cried Constance.

She shouted at the children. She tried to run, but she fell into the big hole and the cement fell on top of her. There was a terrible cry, and Constance the Giantess died.

'So, I finished the house,' Mr. Nebbercracker said to DJ. 'She died, but she didn't leave. She hates children and she's often angry at them. I try to stop her. At Halloween it's very hard.'

The house started to make loud sounds.

'I'm coming, my love,' said Mr. Nebbercracker. 'And you children must go.'

But DJ held his arm. 'No, Mr. Nebbercracker. You have your life. It's time to leave Constance.'

'She's all I have,' said Mr. Nebbercracker sadly.

'No,' said DJ. 'You have me, too. I'm your friend.' He took Mr. Nebbercracker's hand and they walked away.

Mr. Nebbercracker was happy, but the house wasn't. It was very, very angry. Suddenly there was a terrible sound. DJ and Mr. Nebbercracker looked back. The house was moving again!

Chapter 7
Goodbye, Constance!

Mr. Nebbercracker and the three kids ran to the Danger Zone. The house was behind them. It was angry. It was strong. And it was close! Mr. Nebbercracker threw hard bits of cement at the house. 'Stay away from them!' he shouted.

Constance saw Mr. Nebbercracker and stopped. She was quiet.

'You were a bad girl,' said Mr. Nebbercracker. 'I must do this.' He carefully took some dynamite from his bag.

Constance saw it and gave an angry cry. Suddenly there were lights and a loud sound. It was the big digger, and Chowder was the driver.

'How did you learn to drive this?' Jenny asked Chowder.

'I didn't!' answered Chowder.

DJ ran to Mr. Nebbercracker. He gave DJ the dynamite. 'Take this,' he said. 'I started it. You finish it. The dynamite's ready. You have three minutes and eighteen seconds.'

DJ looked at the house. 'Where do I throw it?' he thought. Then he saw the smoke and remembered the fire – the heart.

The digger and the house were now face to face. Then DJ saw the tall crane, high over the Danger Zone.

'Chowder,' he shouted. 'Try to move the house under the crane!'

Suddenly the digger turned and moved to the crane. The house tried to turn but it fell. There was a loud sound. The house started to break. There were parts of the house all over the Danger Zone.

DJ and Jenny went up in the crane. But where was Chowder?

Then they heard him. 'Hey,' shouted Chowder. 'I did it. Me! The house is dead!'

But it wasn't dead. All the parts of the house came back together again to make a new house. This time it was a worse monster than before. It looked terrible.

Chowder drove the digger quickly to the crane. The new monster house followed. The door opened and the mouth closed on the arm of the digger. It took the digger up high. Chowder fell out and then the tongue took the digger. Chowder ran. The house followed.

DJ looked down the arm of the crane. He was frightened. 'I can't do it!' he said.

'You can,' said Jenny and she smiled at him.

'Yes,' he thought, 'I can.' He moved to the end of the arm.

DJ looked down. There was the house. There was the smoke. DJ threw the dynamite into the smoke – into the heart of the house.

Everything was very quiet. The house didn't move. It didn't look like a monster house now. It looked clean and quiet like before. The kids waited. Was it over? Did DJ throw the dynamite in the right place?

Little sounds started to come from the house. Then they were bigger and louder. Suddenly there was a great white light and the house was a ball of fire. Cement, windows, walls and floor rained down from the sky.

The kids shouted and danced. 'We did it. The house is dead!'

Then something happened. A strong wind came and moved all the parts of the house. They all came together in the sky. It was Constance, big and beautiful again.

'Constance,' said DJ quietly.

Mr. Nebbercracker looked up. 'My love, goodbye,' he cried.

Constance smiled. She put her arms around Mr. Nebbercracker. Then the wind came again, and there was only the sky.

'I'm sorry about your …house … erm … wife,' said DJ.

'Constance is happy now,' said Mr. Nebbercracker. There was a light in his eyes. 'And I can live my life. Thank you.'

It was Halloween night. There were trick-or-treaters on Mr. Nebbercracker's lawn. They came to get their things.

There were bikes, basketballs, footballs and kites.

DJ gave the bike back to the little girl.

'Thank you,' she said and smiled. Then she went between the trees and the lovely gardens of Oak Street.

Jenny put her arms around the boys. 'We must do something together again soon,' she said. Then she left with her mom.

'We are too old for treat-or-treating,' said Chowder.

'Yes,' said DJ.

'But we had a very difficult evening.'

'Yes,' said DJ.

'Time for treats?'

'Yeah. Time for treats!' And the boys ran down the road.

Some people came out of the big hole in Mr. Nebbercracker's garden. Bones was first. He looked very surprised. Then the two policemen came out. Bones looked at them. 'Happy Halloween,' he said and smiled. He held his red kite in his hands.

'You, too,' said Landers. 'Happy Halloween!'

HALLOWEEN
AROUND THE WORLD

The story of *Monster House* happens around Halloween (31st October). Mr Nebbercracker's wife, Constance, died on 31st October and the 'monster house' is very angry on this day every year.

Halloween is a very big festival in the USA. In some other countries, too, there are festivals around this time of year. Some people believe the dead can come back to the world. Do you think this is true? What do you know about these festivals?

> Do you have a festival like Halloween in your country? What do you do? What do you eat? What do you wear?

Samhain in Ireland

Halloween started in Ireland many hundreds of years ago. At that time its name was 'Samhain Night'. It was a festival of fire. The dead came back to the world at this time.

A 'pooky' dancing

In Ireland today Halloween is still very important. Children wear special Halloween clothes and go to other people's homes for chocolates, fruit and other treats.

There are also Halloween parties with music and games, and many homes have pumpkin lanterns. In some parts of Ireland people call Halloween 'Pooky Night.' A 'pooky' is a bad spirit.

Halloween in the USA

Ireland was very poor in 1845 and there was no food. Many Irish people went to the USA. They took the festival of Halloween with them.

Halloween is now a very big festival in the USA – only Christmas is bigger. Children wear Halloween clothes and they go trick-or-treating. People put pumpkin lanterns in front of their houses.

Children trick-or-treating

There are also special Halloween parades. The Village Halloween Parade in New York City is the biggest with two million people (and four million people watch it on TV!).

The Day of the Dead in Mexico

From 28th October to 2nd November is a very special time in Mexico. People think about the dead then. But it is not a sad time – it is a time for fun, music and colour.

People go to their family graves. They clean the graves and put flowers and treats on them.

There are also parades and people wear special clothes. Skeletons are a very important part of this festival. Mexican people aren't frightened of skeletons – they think the skeletons are funny!

A parade with skeletons

What do these words mean? You can use a dictionary.
festival   pumpkin lantern   spirit   parade   grave   skeleton

STRANGE HOUSES... TRUE STORIES?

Monster House is a very exciting film about a very strange house. Here are some interesting stories about strange houses. Do you think they are true?

Winchester House

Sarah Winchester was very sad when her husband and young daughter died. She started to talk to spirits. They said to her, 'Build a big house for the spirits of dead people. You must always build or you are going to die!'

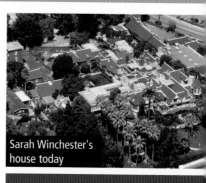

Sarah Winchester's house today

In 1884 Sarah bought a small house. She told some builders, 'Please build more rooms.' The builders worked on the house all day and every day for 38 years. Sarah wanted to trick bad spirits. Some stairs end at the walls and some doors open into the sky.

And you can see the number 13 in lots of places. Sarah died in 1922 and then the builders stopped. By then the house had 160 rooms!

The Whaley House

In 1856 workers started on a new home for Thomas Whaley and his family. Thomas was a rich man. He wanted the house

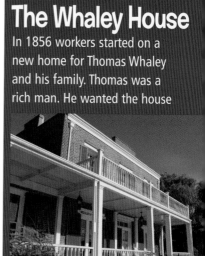

The Coral Castle

Ed Leedskalnin was in love with Agnes Scuffs. He wanted Agnes to be his wife. But just before their special day, Agnes thought, 'I don't want to be Ed's wife. He's too poor.' Ed was very sad. He wanted to do something special to remember his true love. He started to make a special building – the 'Coral Castle'.

Ed was a very small man, but he worked almost alone on the house. He used around 1000 tonnes of rock! He worked only with his hands and some small hand tools. He usually worked at night so no one saw him. Many people asked, 'How can one small man build this great house? He must have special powers!'

to be big with lots of expensive things. But a bad man – 'Yankee Jim' James – died in a terrible way there, some years before.

In 1857 Thomas and his family moved into their new home. But life at the Whaley House was not very happy. One of their children died before he was two. A friend of the children, a young girl, also died there. And the Whaleys started to see the spirits of dead people in the house – 'Yankee Jim' on the stairs, a young girl in the kitchen. And there were strange noises and cold places.

Windows opened and closed when no one was there.

Today many people can still see and feel these strange spirits. And many people think it is one of the strangest houses in the world.

> Do you believe the stories about these strange houses? Where are these houses? Can you find any more information about them?

> What do these words mean? You can use a dictionary.
> spirit   build   rock   tool   power

THE CIRCUS

Constance the Giantess lived in a circus before Mr. Nebbercracker found her. In the past, circuses often had shows with people like Constance. These shows were very cruel and they stopped a long time ago.

When was the first circus?

The first circus was the Circus Maximus in Rome around 2,000 years ago. People went there to watch horse races. They also saw unusual animals, acrobats and special performers.

How did circuses change?

☛ For a long time after the Romans there were no large circuses. But performers went to different towns and gave small shows.

☛ In 1768 Philip Astley opened one of the first circuses in London. Most of his shows were with horses. For many he is the 'father' of today's circus.

☛ In the 1800s circuses started in the USA. In 1835 P. T. Barnum started to use shows with unusual people.

☛ In 1927 the Moscow Circus School

What do you think about circuses?
Do you want to be a circus performer?

started. In the 1950s Russian circuses went to other countries. The acrobats were fantastic!

☞ In the 1960s and 1970s there weren't so many circuses. People weren't happy about animals in shows because it was cruel.

What is the circus like today?

The circus today is different from in the past. Some circuses still have animals (usually just horses), but most circuses just have people in their shows. These people can do fantastic and unusual things. The Cirque du Soleil is a very famous circus like this.

The Cirque du Soleil

The Cirque du Soleil ('Circus of the Sun') started in Canada in 1984. It is famous and very special because each show tells a story. It uses music, special lights and fantastic performers.

At first it moved round the world. Now some shows go to different countries, but the Cirque du Soleil's main home is in Las Vegas.

Acrobats in the Cirque du Soleil

Do you want to be in the circus?

CIRCUS SMIRKUS is a very special circus school. It started in 1987 in Vermont, USA. Young people go to Circus Smirkus in their school holidays and learn to be circus performers. Every summer Circus Smirkus has a show with the best performers from the school. They perform in more than 70 shows in 14 towns in 7 weeks!

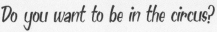

```
What do these words mean?
You can use a dictionary.
show   cruel   horse race   unusual
animal   acrobat   perform/performer
```

Chapters 1-3

Before you read

You can use your dictionary for these questions.

1 Where can we find these things?

lawn   kite   throat   carpet

a) outside the house

b) on the floor

c) in the body

d) in the sky

2 Put the words in the past.

a) *hold* Mr. Nebbercracker ... DJ's shirt.

b) *throw* Chowder ... the ball into the basket.

c) *fall* Mr.Nebbercracker ... onto the lawn.

After you read

3 Choose the correct words.

a) Mr. Nebbercracker takes the little girl's *bike / ball*.

b) DJ has a dream about *school / the house*.

c) DJ phones *his mom / Chowder*.

d) Bones throws a *kite / trainer* on Mr. Nebbercracker's lawn.

e) The *carpet / window* comes out of the house.

f) Jenny is selling *chocolates / newspapers*.

g) A *cat / dog* walks on the lawn.

4 What do you think?

a) Does a monster live in Mr. Nebbercracker's house?

b) Is Mr. Nebbercracker a monster?

c) Why does he take the children's things?

d) Is the house going to eat more people? Who?

5 In your country, do children go trick-or-treating at Halloween? What do they do?

Chapters 4–5

Before you read

6 Complete the sentences with these words.

caravan   cement   heart   circus   smoke

a) Children often think the … is exciting.

b) Some people stay in a … for their holidays.

c) The house was on fire and there was a lot of … in the sky.

d) You use … to make a strong floor in a building.

e) The old man's … was not very strong and he died.

After you read

7 Answer these questions.

a) What did Skull play in the Pizza Freek?

b) What was the heart of the house?

c) Why did the kids put Sleep Easy in the carpet cleaner?

d) Where did the policemen put the kids?

e) How did the kids get inside the house?

f) What did they find in the big room?

g) What was in the cement floor?

h) Who was Constance?

8 Complete the sentences with the names.

Skull   Chowder   Constance   Jenny   DJ

a) … holds onto DJ's legs.

b) … tells them about Domus Mactabilis.

c) … lived in a circus.

d) … doesn't want to go into the house.

e) … has a plan.

9 What do you think?

a) Why is there a body in the floor?

b) Why is Constance angry when people go near her?

Chapters 6-7

Before you read

10 Complete the sentences with these words.

cranes   diggers   dynamite

a) People use ... to make holes in things.

b) People use ... to lift very big things.

c) People use ... to dig holes for buildings.

After you read

11 Put Constance's story in the right order.

a) Mr. Nebbercracker starts to build a house.

b) A boy throws vegetables at Constance.

c) Mr. Nebbercracker finishes the house.

d) Children throw things at Constance.

e) Constance is alone and sad.

f) Constance falls into the hole.

g) Mr. Nebbercracker takes Constance away from the circus.

h) Mr. Nebbercracker stops a boy with old vegetables.

12 Choose the right answer.

a) The kids ran to ... .
   i the Pizza Freek   ii the Danger Zone   iii DJ's house

b) Mr. Nebbercracker gives the dynamite to ...
   i Chowder   ii Jenny   iii DJ

c) Mr. Nebbercracker throws ... at the house.
   i his shoe   ii bits of cement   iii his bag

d) DJ throws the dynamite into ... .
   i the smoke   ii the window   iii the door

e) The first person out of the hole is ... .
   i Landers   ii Lister   iii Bones

13 What do you think?

a) Is DJ going to meet Jenny again?

b) Where is Mr. Nebbercracker going to live?

c) Is Constance going to come back again?

d) Are there really monsters in the world?